Maths BOOSTER

Year 6

Peter Patilla

EDUCATIONAL

Teachers' notes and answers may be viewed and downloaded free of charge from: **www.letts-education.com**

First published 2001

Letts Educational, The Chiswick Centre, 414 Chiswick High Road, London W4 5TF
Telephone: (020) 8996 3333
Fax: (020) 8742 8390
www.letts-education.com

Author: Peter Patilla

Series project editor: Nancy Terry

Series designer: Ken Vail Graphic Design, Cambridge

Illustrations: Chantal Kees

British Library Cataloguing in Publication Data
A CIP record for this book is available from the British Library.

ISBN 1840855908

Printed in the UK.

Reprographics by PDQ.

Letts Educational, a division of Granada learning Ltd.
Part of the Granada Media Group.

Maths BOOSTER

Year 6

Contents

Place value 1

Warm up

What is the value of the coloured digit?

1 23 674

   a 2000   b 20 000   c 200 000

2 759 024

   a 5000   b 50 000   c 500 000

3 1 657 400

   a 60 000   b 600 000   c 6 000 000

4 7 138 421

   a 70 000   b 700   c 7 000 000

A

Write how much the coloured digit is worth.

1 32.425

2 1.625

3 140.36

4 0.5025

5 2.8876

Write the difference in value between the digits.

6 3.424

7 0.0443

8 40.64

9 24.004

10 3.4124

The first place of decimals are tenths.
The second place are hundredths.
The third place are thousandths.
The fourth place are ten thousandths.

3.1255

units
tenths
hundredths
thousandths
ten thousandths

Decimals do not stop after four places. They can go on and on like this: 3.12370975 …

B

Copy and write <, > or = between each pair.

1 4.04 ☐ 4.40

2 7.007 ☐ 7.07

3 0.050 ☐ 0.005

4 1.01 ☐ 1.0100

5 0.200 ☐ 0.0200

6 2.020 ☐ 2.200

7 0.025 ☐ 0.052

8 0.720 ☐ 0.0720

9 1.04 ☐ 1.04000

10 3.050 ☐ 3.005

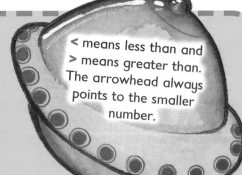

< means less than and > means greater than. The arrowhead always points to the smaller number.

C

Use these digits.

0   1   4   6

They go in these boxes to make a number between 1.5 and 1.75.
Write which two numbers can be made.

Place value 2

Multiply each amount by 10.

1 £7.00
  a £7
  b £70
  c £700

2 £0.70
  a £7
  b £70
  c £700

3 £0.07
  a 7p
  b 70p
  c 700p

A

Multiply each number by 10.	Multiply each number by 100.	Multiply each number by 1000.
1 7.0	6 0.2	11 0.030
2 0.70	7 2.00	12 0.003
3 70.0	8 0.002	13 30.00
4 0.07	9 20.0	14 3.0
5 0.007	10 0.20	15 0.300

Multiplying by 10, 100 or 1000 makes the digits move to the left.

←

A common mistake is to just to add zeros.

B

Remember, dividing by 10, 100 or 1000 makes the digits move to the right.

→

A common mistake is to just to remove zeros.

Divide each number by 10.	Divide each number by 100.	Divide each number by 1000.
1 7.0	6 0.2	11 3.0
2 70.00	7 2.00	12 30.00
3 0.700	8 20.0	13 0.30
4 700.0	9 200.0	14 300
5 0.07	10 0.020	15 0.003

C What are the missing numbers?

$$0.8 \times \boxed{} = 80.00 \qquad 4.0 \div \boxed{} = 0.0040$$

Rounding 1

Round each amount to the nearest pound.

1 **£6.62**
   a £6
   b £7
   c £66

2 **£14.09**
   a £14
   b £15
   c £140

3 **£126.49**
   a £12
   b £126
   c £127

A

Round each number to a sensible amount.
Rewrite each sentence using approximation words.

1 16 813 people attended the match.

2 Gregory is 98.125 cm tall.

3 The new window cost £129.99.

4 The aeroplane flew 12 113 km.

5 The book is 8.5125 cm thick.

6 The parcel weighed 127.9 grams.

7 The container held 4.099 litres.

8 The population was 12 477 312.

Sometimes you have to choose a sensible number to round to.

Approximation words include: *about, nearly, just under, just over, approximately, roughly.*

B

Round these to one decimal place.

1 4.765

2 0.618

3 12.953

4 0.1265

5 125.95

Round these to two decimal places.

6 0.1245

7 12.338

8 20.0604

9 32.497

10 0.995

Sometimes you need to round to one or two decimal places.

2.446 to **one decimal place** is 2.4
2.446 to **two decimal places** is 2.45

Sometimes there is a knock on to the next column.

3.96 to one decimal place is 4.0

C

Write each of these amounts to two decimal places.

15.314 metres   6.625 metres

Rounding 2

Round each amount to the nearest kilogram.

1 **4.507 kg**
   a 4 kg
   b 5 kg
   c 45 kg

2 **3.009 kg**
   a 3 kg
   b 4 kg
   c 30 kg

3 **12.702 kg**
   a 127 kg
   b 12 kg
   c 13 kg

A

Round these to the nearest metre.

1 5675 cm

2 835.6 cm

3 0.473 km

4 3425 mm

Round these to the nearest kilogram.

5 2784 g

6 987.4 g

7 3077.8 g

8 0.452 tonnes

Round these to the nearest litre.

9 3099 mℓ

10 1502.75 mℓ

11 458.7 cℓ

12 72.3 dℓ

> When using measurements, look at the units very carefully. It is very easy to work in the wrong units.
> • LOOK at the UNITS
> • CHOOSE which to work in.

B

Round these to the nearest half metre.

1 5.76 m

2 6.12 m

3 4.63 m

4 7.82 m

5 258 cm

6 875 cm

7 323 cm

8 669 cm

9 107.5 cm

10 455.7 cm

11 364.9 cm

12 897.2 cm

> Sometimes you round to the nearest half unit. When a measurement is between the half and the whole unit:
> • round up if it is more than halfway
> • round down if it is less than halfway.
>   2.74 m ≈ 2.5 m (round down)
>   4.22 m ≈ 4.0 m (round down)
>   5.83 m ≈ 6.0 m (round up)

C

What is the reading to the nearest half kilogram?

Approximation 1

Round each amount to the nearest pound.

1 (£6.62)
   a £6
   b £7
   c £66

2 (£14.09)
   a £14
   b £15
   c £140

3 (£126.49)
   a £12
   b £126
   c £127

A What is a sensible approximation for each calculation?

1 $608 - 198$

2 $1067 - 789$

3 $3411 - 1752$

4 $12345 - 9699$

5 $23145 - 869$

6 $40256 - 7177$

7 $2789 + 5127$

8 $13294 + 584$

9 $22895 + 4253$

10 $34604 + 23671$

11 $74986 + 25799$

12 $375683 + 452130$

- You can check for silly mistakes by approximating answers.
- Round each number to a sensible number.
- Then you must be able to work out the approximate calculation in your head.

Example: $715 - 382 \approx 700 - 400$
The approximate answer will be 300.

B What is a sensible approximation for each decimal calculation?

1 $6.196 + 3.09$

2 $12.705 + 8.936$

3 $134.27 + 8.6088$

4 $0.876 + 0.419$

5 $0.328 + 0.99$

6 $0.853 + 0.3612$

7 $5.287 - 2.697$

8 $8.056 - 2.877$

9 $6.20 - 3.877$

10 $0.4 - 0.127$

11 $0.956 - 0.27$

12 $0.750 - 0.089$

- You can use approximating in just the same way when working with decimal numbers.
- Choose an approximation that you can work out in your head.

Example: $5.267 + 2.81 \approx 5.0 + 3.0$
The approximate answer will be 8.0.

C

Mrs Leadbetter exchanged a coat that cost her £49.99 for one that cost £79.99.
At the same time she bought a pair of shoes costing £37.49.
How much did she spend in total?

£167.47   £67.49   £104.99   £20.47

Approximation 2

Round each distance to the nearest kilometre.

1. **9.08 km**
   - a 8 km
   - b 9 km
   - c 90 km

2. **39.54 km**
   - a 30 km
   - b 39 km
   - c 40 km

3. **299.75 km**
   - a 290 km
   - b 299 km
   - c 300 km

A

What is a sensible approximation for each calculation?

1. 51×49
2. 72×88
3. 93×19
4. 127×78
5. 208×37
6. 898×52
7. 332×187
8. 634×277
9. 631×208
10. 8477×47
11. 6426×386
12. 8751×741

- Round each number to a sensible number.
- **You must choose numbers that help you to work out the approximate calculation in your head.**

  Example: $23 \times 78 \approx 20 \times 80$, so the approximate answer will be 1600.

  Example: $368 \times 42 \approx 400 \times 40$, so the approximate answer will be 16 000.

B

- Approximating is a little more complicated when dividing.
- You might have to do two approximations.

  Example: $827 \div 68 \approx 800 \div 70$
  The approximate answer will be about 11.

  Example: $3863 \div 32 \approx 4000 \div 30$
  The approximate answer will be about 130.

- **Remember, you must be able to work out the approximate calculation in your head.**

What is a sensible approximation for each division?

1. $714 \div 54$
2. $693 \div 19$
3. $406 \div 79$
4. $2067 \div 88$
5. $3276 \div 59$
6. $6602 \div 16$
7. $3672 \div 204$
8. $7632 \div 199$
9. $5098 \div 345$
10. $12\,189 \div 69$
11. $35\,677 \div 85$
12. $24\,640 \div 291$

C

Mr Patel bought 56 cases of tinned fruit. Each case cost £28.67. How much did he spend in total?

£605.52   £1605.52   £2605.52   £3605.52

Approximation 3

Warm up

Answer these decimal calculations.

1 **0.6 × 0.4**
   a 24
   b 2.4
   c 0.24

2 **0.7 × 0.5**
   a 3.5
   b 0.35
   c 35

3 **0.8 × 0.8**
   a 6.4
   b 64
   c 0.64

A

What is a sensible approximation for each multiplication?

1 13.4 × 5.8   5 32.44 × 2.91   9   12.37 × 0.7

2 24.6 × 2.4   6 28.16 × 9.77   10 16.54 × 0.6

3 5.76 × 4.77   7 7.37 × 0.5   11 64.08 × 0.8

4 8.05 × 6.29   8 8.56 × 0.8   12 77.53 × 0.9

- Round each decimal to a sensible number.
- **You must choose numbers that let you work out the approximate calculation in your head.**
     Example: 12.4 × 8.9 ≈ 12 × 9, so the approximate answer will be 108.
     Example 2.67 × 0.8 ≈ 3 × 0.8, so the approximate answer will be 2.4.

B

What is a sensible approximation for each division?

1 44.1 ÷ 5.6   7   27.22 ÷ 2.04

2 36.6 ÷ 7.2   8   41.84 ÷ 2.85

3 55.2 ÷ 3.5   9   126.3 ÷ 5.6

4 25.45 ÷ 7.4   10 605.7 ÷ 6.9

5 32.76 ÷ 5.9   11 634.6 ÷ 8.2

6 70.38 ÷ 1.6   12 125.6 ÷ 2.91

- Approximating is a little more complicated when dividing with decimals.
- You might have to do two approximations.
     Example: 24.6 ÷ 8.3 ≈ 25 ÷ 8
     The answer will be about 3.
- **Remember, you must be able to work out the approximate calculation in your head.**

C

Write which of these is the area of the rectangle.

22.622 cm^2 94.622 cm^2 168.622 cm^2

12.65 cm

7.48 cm

Integers

Warm up — To which number does the arrow point?

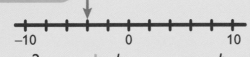

1.

a 2   b 4   c −4

3.
a 3   b −3   c −2

2.
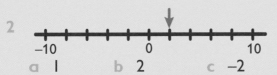
a 1   b 2   c −2

4.
a 3½   b 7   c −7

A

Which integers could go in the boxes?

1 −4 < ☐ < 0

2 −6 < ☐ < −3

3 −3 < ☐ < 2

4 −22 < ☐ < −18

5 −7 < ☐ < 3

Which even integers could go in the boxes?

6 −5 < ☐ < 0

7 −6 < ☐ < −2

8 −3 < ☐ < 3

9 − 7 < ☐ < −11

10 −7 < ☐ < 6

- All whole numbers are called **integers**.
- Integers can be **positive** or **negative**.
- Zero is an integer.
- When you move left on a number line, numbers get smaller.
- When you move right on a number line, numbers get larger.

  Example: −3 is less than −2,
  2 is more than −5

B

Which integers could go in the boxes?

1 −3 ≤ ☐ ≤ 0

2 −7 ≤ ☐ ≤ −4

3 −5 ≤ ☐ ≤ 1

4 −11 ≤ ☐ ≤ −9

5 −5 ≤ ☐ ≤ 3

Which odd integers could go in the boxes?

6 0 ≥ ☐ ≥ −5

7 −2 ≥ ☐ ≥ −6

8 3 ≥ ☐ ≥ −3

9 −11 ≥ ☐ ≥ −17

10 6 ≥ ☐ ≥ − 7

≤ means 'less than or equals' and ≥ means 'more than or equals'. In the statement 6 ≤ ☐ ≥ 9, the integers 6, 7, 8 or 9 could go in the box.

C Write these six integers in order. Start with the smallest.

−20   7   −2   0   −15   15

Negative numbers

1
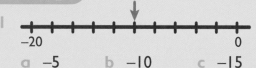
−20   0

a −5   b −10   c −15

3
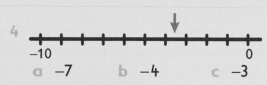
−20   0

a −2   b −4   c −8

2
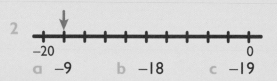
−20   0

a −9   b −18   c −19

4

−10   0

a −7   b −4   c −3

A To which number does the arrow point?

1
−10   0

4
−5   0

2
−10   0

5
−1   0

3
−5   0

6
−2   0

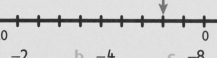

Negative numbers are not always whole numbers. They can be fractions or decimals.

Remember to work out what each mark on the number line stands for.

B

Negative numbers can also be used in measuring.

Check the units you work in very carefully.

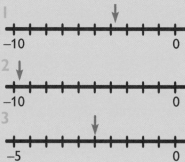

Wilf was trying to throw a coin exactly 2 metres. He recorded each attempt in centimetres above or below his target:

1st	2nd	3rd	4th	5th	6th	7th	8th
+3	+5.5	−2	−7	−1.5	0	+0.5	−0.5

1 What was his longest throw?

2 What was his shortest throw?

3 On which attempt did he hit his target?

4 On which attempt did he throw 198.5 cm?

5 How would he have recorded a throw of 1.96 m?

C The temperature is −4°C.
It rises by 8 degrees then drops by 3 degrees.
What is the temperature now?

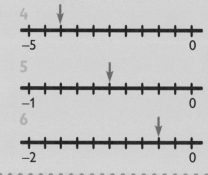

Fractions 1

Which fraction is equivalent to each of these?

1. $\frac{2}{3}$
   a $\frac{3}{6}$
   b $\frac{4}{9}$
   c $\frac{4}{6}$

2. $\frac{3}{4}$
   a $\frac{6}{12}$
   b $\frac{6}{8}$
   c $\frac{6}{16}$

3. $\frac{4}{5}$
   a $\frac{12}{20}$
   b $\frac{8}{15}$
   c $\frac{8}{10}$

A

1 Change $\frac{3}{5}$ into tenths.

2 Change $\frac{4}{5}$ into hundredths.

3 Change $\frac{3}{8}$ into sixteenths.

4 Change $\frac{3}{4}$ into twelfths.

5 Change $\frac{2}{5}$ into hundredths.

6 Change $\frac{12}{16}$ into eighths.

7 Change $\frac{12}{16}$ into quarters.

8 Change $\frac{40}{100}$ into tenths.

9 Change $\frac{40}{100}$ into fifths.

10 Change $\frac{16}{20}$ into tenths.

If you multiply or divide the numerator and denominator by the same number, the fractions will be equivalent:

$$\frac{12 \div 4}{16 \div 4} = \frac{3}{4} \qquad \frac{4 \times 4}{5 \times 4} = \frac{16}{20}$$

B

When you divide the numerator and denominator by the same number, you are cancelling the fraction. Sometimes you can cancel a fraction more than once.

When you can cancel no more, the fraction is as simple as possible.

$$\frac{12 \div 2}{16 \div 2} = \frac{6 \div 2}{8 \div 2} = \frac{3}{4}$$

Cancel each fraction to make it as simple as possible.

1 $\frac{60}{100}$

2 $\frac{16}{20}$

3 $\frac{30}{50}$

4 $\frac{12}{16}$

5 $\frac{85}{100}$

6 $\frac{18}{24}$

7 $\frac{12}{18}$

8 $\frac{24}{64}$

9 $\frac{24}{100}$

10 $\frac{64}{100}$

C

Write an equivalent fraction for these.
Each denominator must be the same and as small as possible.

$$\frac{2}{3} \qquad \frac{3}{4} \qquad \frac{5}{8}$$

Fractions 2

Which mixed number matches the improper fraction?

1 $\frac{14}{3}$
   a $3\frac{2}{3}$
   b $4\frac{1}{3}$
   c $4\frac{2}{3}$

2 $\frac{15}{4}$
   a $2\frac{3}{4}$
   b $3\frac{3}{4}$
   c $3\frac{1}{4}$

2 $\frac{24}{5}$
   a $4\frac{2}{5}$
   b $4\frac{3}{5}$
   c $4\frac{4}{5}$

A

Write each improper fraction as a mixed fraction.
Make each fraction as simple as possible.

1 $\frac{28}{8}$ 5 $\frac{36}{8}$ 9 $\frac{74}{10}$

2 $\frac{27}{6}$ 6 $\frac{65}{10}$ 10 $\frac{54}{12}$

3 $\frac{36}{10}$ 7 $\frac{39}{12}$ 11 $\frac{60}{16}$

4 $\frac{33}{6}$ 8 $\frac{34}{16}$ 12 $\frac{185}{20}$

> You can cancel improper fractions before or after you have changed them into a mixed number.
>
> Before $\frac{26}{8} \genfrac{}{}{0pt}{}{\div 2}{\div 2} = \frac{13}{4} = 3\frac{1}{4}$
>
> After $\frac{26}{8} = 3\frac{2}{8} \genfrac{}{}{0pt}{}{\div 2}{\div 2} = 3\frac{1}{4}$

B

Write each quotient as a fraction.
Make each fraction as simple as possible.

1 $74 \div 8$ 5 $91 \div 14$ 9 $186 \div 18$

2 $86 \div 6$ 6 $165 \div 20$ 10 $152 \div 24$

3 $68 \div 12$ 7 $164 \div 16$ 11 $184 \div 20$

4 $56 \div 16$ 8 $147 \div 12$ 12 $153 \div 36$

> A fraction is another way of writing a division.
>
> $26 \div 8 = \frac{26}{8} = \frac{13}{4} = 3\frac{1}{4}$
>
> $3\frac{1}{4}$ is the **quotient** of $26 \div 8$ with the fraction as simple as possible.

C

Write which quotient matches the division $128 \div 12$.

$10\frac{3}{4}$ $10\frac{2}{3}$ $10\frac{1}{6}$ $10\frac{3}{8}$

Special numbers

Warm up   What is the square of each number?

1. **11**
   - a 111
   - b 122
   - c 121

2. **13**
   - a 126
   - b 169
   - c 139

3. **15**
   - a 225
   - b 250
   - c 215

A

What are these squares?

1. 14^2
2. 16^2
3. 17^2
4. 18^2
5. 22^2
6. 25^2
7. 36^2
8. 72^2

What are these square roots?

9. $\sqrt{64}$
10. $\sqrt{81}$
11. $\sqrt{49}$
12. $\sqrt{36}$
13. $\sqrt{144}$
14. $\sqrt{400}$
15. $\sqrt{1000}$
16. $\sqrt{169}$

> A square number is the result of multiplying a number by itself:
> $12^2 = 144$
>
> A square root is the opposite of a square. The sign for square root is $\sqrt{}$:
> $\sqrt{144} = 12$

B

What are the prime factors of these numbers?

1. 20
2. 28
3. 36
4. 40
5. 60

These sequences are consecutive prime numbers with last digits missing.
What are the numbers?

6	37	4*	4*	4*	5*	5*
7	71	7*	7*	8*	8*	9*

> A **prime number** is any number that only has two factors: itself and 1.
> The prime numbers less than 20 are:
> 2, 3, 5, 7, 11, 13, 17, 19
> 1 is not a prime number.

C

Copy the diagram.
Write these numbers on your diagram.

81   83   91   93   97

prime numbers   square numbers

Decimals 1

What is the value of the coloured digit?

1 0.3 7 6
a $\frac{7}{10}$
b $\frac{7}{100}$
c $\frac{7}{1000}$

2 4. 6 25
a $\frac{6}{10}$
b $\frac{6}{100}$
c $\frac{6}{1000}$

3 37.48 5
a $\frac{5}{10}$
b $\frac{5}{100}$
c $\frac{5}{1000}$

A Write the quotients as decimals.

1 $\frac{3}{8}$

2 $\frac{7}{5}$

3 $\frac{11}{8}$

4 $\frac{17}{4}$

5 $\frac{21}{6}$

6 $32 \div 5$

7 $51 \div 8$

8 $54 \div 12$

9 $36 \div 16$

10 $91 \div 20$

A fraction is another way of writing a division.

$$\frac{5}{8} = 8\overline{)5.000} = 8\overline{)5.000}^{\,0.625}$$

0.625 is the **decimal quotient** of $5 \div 8$

B What are the decimal quotients?
Stop at five decimal places.

1 $11 \div 3$

2 $13 \div 6$

3 $17 \div 7$

4 $22 \div 9$

5 $30 \div 11$

6 Solve this problem: Which members of the twelfth family of fractions does not have a recurring decimal quotient? Can you find a rule?

$8 \div 3$ is a division that does not have an exact decimal quotient.

$$3\overline{)8.0000} \rightarrow \;\; 2.6666 \rightarrow$$

The quotient is a **recurring decimal** that goes on and on without ending.

C Write down these three divisons:

$37 \div 8$ $14 \div 3$ $33 \div 7$

Match each division to one of these quotients:

4.71428   4.62500   4.66666

Decimals 2

Which decimal matches the fraction?

1. $\frac{5}{8}$
   - a   0.125
   - b   0.375
   - c   0.625

2. $\frac{4}{5}$
   - a   0.008
   - b   0.080
   - c   0.800

3. $\frac{2}{3}$
   - a   0.333
   - b   0.666
   - c   0.999

A

Only use one operation.
What was the calculator input that changed the
first number into the second?

1. $0.002 \rightarrow 0.200$
2. $4.000 \rightarrow 0.040$
3. $0.007 \rightarrow 0.069$
4. $0.500 \rightarrow 0.505$
5. $0.600 \rightarrow 0.006$
6. $0.505 \rightarrow 0.550$
7. $3.006 \rightarrow 0.306$
8. $0.160 \rightarrow 1.600$
9. $7.800 \rightarrow 0.078$
10. $0.303 \rightarrow 3.300$

> There are four operations
> +, −, × and ÷.
> Think which operation has been
> used and the number involved.
>
> $0.001 \rightarrow 0.0011$
>
> The input was + 0.0001.

B

Write each set of fractions in order.
You can use a calculator to help.

1. $\frac{7}{20}$ $\frac{6}{15}$ $\frac{17}{40}$ $\frac{9}{25}$

2. $\frac{2}{3}$ $\frac{4}{7}$ $\frac{5}{11}$ $\frac{7}{9}$

3. $\frac{7}{30}$ $\frac{5}{12}$ $\frac{6}{25}$ $\frac{13}{50}$

4. $\frac{8}{15}$ $\frac{11}{20}$ $\frac{17}{40}$ $\frac{14}{25}$

5. $\frac{6}{7}$ $\frac{7}{8}$ $\frac{9}{11}$ $\frac{10}{13}$

6. $\frac{6}{13}$ $\frac{5}{7}$ $\frac{22}{35}$ $\frac{14}{45}$

> When ordering fractions,
> it helps to change them
> into decimals.
>
> To order these fractions: $\frac{2}{3}$ $\frac{5}{7}$ $\frac{5}{8}$
>
> change them to decimals:
>
> $\frac{2}{3} = 0.666$ $\frac{5}{7} = 0.712$ $\frac{5}{8} = 0.625$
>
> The order is: $\frac{5}{8}$ $\frac{2}{3}$ $\frac{5}{7}$

C

Copy the fractions.
Write < or > between them.

$\frac{3}{4}$ ☐ $\frac{11}{14}$

Fractions, decimals and percentages

Warm up What is each percentage as a fraction?

1 **20%**
  a $\frac{1}{3}$
  b $\frac{1}{5}$
  c $\frac{1}{20}$

2 **15%**
  a $\frac{1}{15}$
  b $\frac{3}{5}$
  c $\frac{3}{20}$

3 **8%**
  a $\frac{2}{25}$
  b $\frac{1}{5}$
  c $\frac{3}{20}$

A Choose which percentage approximately matches the fraction.

1 $\frac{1}{8} \approx$ 20% 12% 15%

2 $\frac{1}{7} \approx$ 14% 19% 21%

3 $\frac{1}{12} \approx$ 5% 8% 12%

4 $\frac{1}{15} \approx$ 2% 5% 7%

5 $\frac{7}{8} \approx$ 66% 77% 88%

6 $\frac{4}{7} \approx$ 47% 57% 67%

7 $\frac{5}{12} \approx$ 42% 52% 62%

8 $\frac{7}{15} \approx$ 37% 47% 57%

Thirds do not always change exactly into decimals or percentages:

$\frac{1}{3} = 0.333 = 33\frac{1}{3}\% = 33.333\%$

$\frac{2}{3} = 0.667 = 66\frac{2}{3}\% = 66.667\%$

$\frac{1}{3} \approx 33\%$ $\frac{2}{3} \approx 67\%$

B Look at the decimal.
Choose an equivalent percentage.

1 0.24 → 0.24% 240% 2.4% 24%

2 0.07 → 0.07% 70% 7% 0.7%

3 0.37 → 0.37% 370% 37% 3.7%

4 2.5 → 0.25% 2.5% 250% 25%

5 4.2 → 0.42% 42% 4.2% 420%

6 1.25 → 125% 12.5% 1.25% 0.125%

Percentages do not have to be whole numbers.

$17\frac{1}{2}\%$ $6\frac{2}{3}\%$ 75.5%   8.625%

Percentages can be more than 100%:

150%   200% $117\frac{1}{2}\%$ $333\frac{1}{3}\%$

C Write this mark as a percentage.
Round the percentage to the nearest whole number.

$$\frac{16}{70}$$

Multiplication tables

Which multiplication fact matches these answers?

1 80
- a 20×0.4
- b 200×0.4
- c 2000×0.4

2 28
- a 70×0.4
- b 700×0.4
- c 7000×0.4

3 240
- a 60×0.4
- b 600×0.4
- c 6000×0.4

A

Try to answer these in your head.

1 800×400
2 60×5000
3 9000×50
4 700×700
5 $50 \times 80\,000$
6 300×120

7 7×0.6
8 30×0.8
9 80×0.7
10 500×0.4
11 900×0.9
12 4000×0.6

13 0.5×0.3
14 0.6×0.6
15 0.3×0.8
16 0.8×0.9
17 0.5×0.8
18 0.7×0.5

You can use multiplication facts you know to work out other facts.

$6 \times 9 = 54$
$60 \times 900 = 54\,000$
$60 \times 0.9 = 54.0$
$0.6 \times 0.9 = 0.54$

Remember to think about the zeros.

B

What are the missing numbers?
Try to work out the answer in your head.

1 $20 \times \boxed{} = 8000$
2 $8 \times \boxed{} = 72\,000$
3 $6000 \times \boxed{} = 30\,000$
4 $700 \times \boxed{} = 3500$
5 $40 \times \boxed{} = 36\,000$
6 $\boxed{} \times 0.3 = 2.4$
7 $\boxed{} \times 0.4 = 2$
8 $\boxed{} \times 0.7 = 21$

9 $\boxed{} \times 0.6 = 240$
10 $\boxed{} \times 0.5 = 45\,000$
11 $0.4 \times \boxed{} = 0.36$
12 $0.8 \times \boxed{} = 0.72$
13 $0.6 \times \boxed{} = 0.54$
14 $\boxed{} \times 0.5 = 0.20$
15 $\boxed{} \times 0.6 = 0.30$
16 $\boxed{} \times 0.1 = 0.01$

Always take a few seconds to check the result in case you have made a silly mistake.

C

Write all the different products you can make using two of these numbers:

0.2   0.5   0.003

Division facts

Warm up Which division fact matches these answers?

1 **3**
  a 240 ÷ 8
  b 2400 ÷ 80
  c 240 ÷ 80

2 **60**
  a 4200 ÷ 70
  b 420 ÷ 70
  c 4200 ÷ 7

3 **600**
  a 480 ÷ 8
  b 48000 ÷ 8
  c 48000 ÷ 80

A

Try to answer these in your head.

1 32000 ÷ 400
2 30000 ÷ 5000
3 45000 ÷ 50
4 490000 ÷ 700
5 400000 ÷ 80000
6 560000 ÷ 80

7 4.2 ÷ 0.6
8 2.4 ÷ 0.8
9 5.6 ÷ 0.7
10 16 ÷ 0.4
11 18 ÷ 0.9
12 24 ÷ 0.6

13 0.15 ÷ 0.3
14 0.24 ÷ 0.6
15 0.32 ÷ 0.8
16 0.81 ÷ 0.9
17 0.40 ÷ 0.5
18 0.80 ÷ 0.8

> You can use division facts you know to work out other facts.
> $54 ÷ 6 = 9$
> $54000 ÷ 60 = 900$
> $54.0 ÷ 60 = 0.9$
> $0.54 ÷ 0.6 = 0.9$
>
> Think about the zeros.

B

What is the missing number?
Try to work out the answer in your head.

1 ☐ ÷ 7 = 0.9
2 ☐ ÷ 9 = 0.5
3 ☐ ÷ 8 = 0.07
4 ☐ ÷ 9 = 0.08
5 ☐ ÷ 6 = 0.07
6 ☐ ÷ 0.3 = 80
7 ☐ ÷ 0.4 = 80
8 ☐ ÷ 0.7 = 60

9 ☐ ÷ 0.6 = 600
10 ☐ ÷ 0.5 = 500
11 ☐ ÷ 0.9 = 0.9
12 ☐ ÷ 0.2 = 0.4
13 ☐ ÷ 0.7 = 0.5
14 ☐ ÷ 0.3 = 0.3
15 ☐ ÷ 0.9 = 0.7
16 ☐ ÷ 0.3 = 0.9

> You can check a division by multiplication.
> $240 ÷ 0.6 = 400$
> Check $400 × 0.6 = 240$

C

Use these numbers: 0.3   0.4   0.12

Write three different multiplication or division calculations that use these numbers.
e.g. $0.3 × 0.4 = 0.12$

Brackets

What is the answer?

1. 100 − (10 − 4)
   a 86
   b 94
   c 84

2. 100 + (5 × 2)
   a 210
   b 110
   c 107

3. 100 ÷ (20 + 5)
   a 4
   b 10
   c 5

A

Work out the missing numbers.

1. (135 ÷ ☐) + 3 = 30
2. (420 ÷ ☐) − 5 = 65
3. (630 ÷ ☐) + 50 = 57
4. (☐ ÷ 5) + 25 = 75
5. (☐ ÷ 3) − 65 = 35

6. (50 × ☐) + 18 = 218
7. (7 × ☐) − 55 = 155
8. (☐ − 15) × 7 = 210
9. (☐ + 15) × 8 = 640
10. (☐ × 3) + 35 = 140

- Work out brackets first.
- Addition and subtraction undo each other.
- Multiplication and division undo each other.
- Always check your answer.

B

Answer these.

1. $\frac{1}{3}$ of 27 − (10 − 4)
2. (3 × 4) + $\frac{3}{4}$ of 16
3. $\frac{1}{2}$ of 24 − $\frac{1}{4}$ of 32
4. $\frac{1}{5}$ of 35 × $\frac{1}{5}$ of 45
5. (9 × 8) ÷ $\frac{1}{10}$ of 30

6. (0.2 × 0.3) + (0.4 × 0.4)
7. (1.4 − 0.8) − (0.2 × 0.2)
8. 1.2 + 8 − (0.81 ÷ 9)
9. (5.6 ÷ 7) + 1.2 − 0.3
10. 1.5 + (0.21 ÷ 0.7) − 0.01

This is the order you should use to work out chain calculations.

Brackets $\frac{1}{2}$ of 16 + (3 × 4)
Of
Division $\frac{1}{2}$ of 16 + 12
Multiplication   8 + 12
Addition   Answer = 20
Subtraction

C

Copy and draw brackets to make this calculation true.

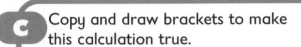

1.0 − 0.3 × 0.4 + 0.02 = 0.9

Equations

What is the missing number?

1 ? — halve then add 5 → 20
  a 20
  b 25
  c 30

2 ? — squared → 9
  a 81
  b 18
  c 3

3 ? — halved then quartered → 4
  a 32
  b 24
  c 168

4 ? — trebled then subtract 4 → 11
  a 21
  b 5
  c 45

A

Which number does each letter stand for?

1 $17 + t = 24$

2 $w + 15 = 36$

3 $m - 13 = 22$

4 $31 - h = 17$

5 $f - 24 = 24$

6 $b \times 3 = 27$

7 $m \times 12 = 48$

8 $7 \times w = 42$

9 $12 \times k = 96$

10 $45 \times n = 135$

11 $\frac{t}{4} = 6$

12 $\frac{w}{6} = 12$

13 $\frac{a}{9} = 30$

14 $\frac{12}{t} = 4$

15 $\frac{36}{d} = 9$

> Sometimes the $\times$ sign is missed out like this:
> $$3 \times t = 3t$$
> $$3t = 24$$
> $$t = 8$$

B

Which number does each letter stand for?

1 $3g = 27$

2 $9p = 108$

3 $6w = 96$

4 $4t = 128$

5 $2h = 7$

6 $2w + 1 = 9$

7 $3m + 2 = 17$

8 $5v + 8 = 38$

9 $15 + 7n = 35$

10 $22 + 9b = 94$

11 $2d - 5 = 15$

12 $4g - 8 = 32$

13 $7m - 3 = 39$

14 $50 - 2h = 44$

15 $75 - 3t = 60$

> In an equation you have to work out which number the letter stands for.
> $$20 - p = 11$$
> $$p = 9$$

C

Which equation describes what the machine does to numbers?

$3p = q$

$p + 3 = q$

$q + 3 = p$

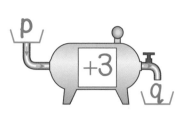

Formulas

1 $30 - T = P$
  a 40
  b 20
  c 10

2 $2T = P$
  a 40
  b 20
  c 10

3 $\frac{T}{2} = P$
  a 40
  b 20
  c 10

A Use the formula for finding area and perimeter of rectangles.

What is A?
1 L = 7 cm B = 5 cm
2 L = 12 cm B = 9 cm
3 L = 8.5 m B = 14 cm

What is L?
7 A = 24 cm² B = 8 cm
8 A = 96 cm² B = 12 cm
9 A = 660 cm² B = 20 cm

What is P?
4 L = 7 cm B = 11 cm
5 L = 23 cm B = 27 cm
6 L = 17 cm B = 24.5 cm

What is B?
10 P = 28 cm L = 7 cm
11 P = 56 cm L = 13 cm
12 P = 90 cm L = 21 cm

> A **formula** uses letters to stand for numbers or measurements. It can help you remember how to work out a calculation.
>
> Formula for area of a rectangle is **A = L × B**
>
> Formula for perimeter of a rectangle is **P = 2 × (L + B)**
>
> A stands for area, P stands for perimeter,
>
> L stands for length, B stands for breadth.

B Write your own formula for each of these.

1 Toyah has N library books and borrows 5 more. What is her total T number of books? T = ☐

2 There are 30 children in a class then Y of them leave. What number N of children remain? N = ☐

3 There are T biscuits on a plate and 6 of them are eaten. How many biscuits K remain? K = ☐

4 £C is shared equally between three children. How pounds P does each receive? P = ☐

> Sometimes you need to work out your own formula.
>
> The formula for the number of weeks W in Y years is W = Y × 52
>
> The formula for the total cost T of N books at £7 each is T = £7 × N

C Fran has X sweets.
She eats two of the sweets then shares the rest between herself and two friends.
Copy and complete this formula to show how many sweets N each friend will receive.   N = ☐

Addition

Warm up
Which answer matches these additions?

1. $2.40 + 3.70$
   - a 5.11
   - b 5.10
   - c 6.10

2. $5.20 + 2.80$
   - a 8.00
   - b 7.10
   - c 7.00

3. $3.90 + 6.40$
   - a 9.30
   - b 9.13
   - c 10.30

A
Calculate the totals.

1. 12476, 8543, 864
2. 236, 16544, 3495
3. £276, £6764, £67
4. 735 km, 10456 km, 84 km
5. 37 kg, 255 kg, 89 kg, 7126 kg
6. 2.45, 0.625, 12.9
7. 135.8, 0.77, 0.338
8. 12.7 m, 5.865 m, 0.75 m
9. £27, £87.77, £6.88, £150
10. 62 km, 88.75 km, 106.5 km

> When adding whole numbers, line up the units.
>
> When adding decimal numbers, line up the decimal points.
>
> $$\begin{array}{r} 3598 \\ 563 \\ + \quad 77 \\ \hline \end{array} \qquad \begin{array}{r} 2.45 \\ 3.136 \\ + 17.2 \\ \hline \end{array}$$

B
What are the missing numbers?

1. $\boxed{} + 2457 = 73004$
2. $\boxed{} + 9456 = 622483$
3. $\boxed{} + 346 + 754 = 12095$
4. $678 + \boxed{} + 59 = 3477$
5. $956 + \boxed{} + 2097 = 78000$
6. $12.35 + \boxed{} = 33.12$
7. $0.276 + \boxed{} = 1.006$
8. $2.65 + \boxed{} + 13.8 = 18.125$
9. $0.625 + \boxed{} + 15.6 = 18.0$
10. $12 + \boxed{} + 7.654 = 22.75$
11. $1.76 m + 88 cm + \boxed{} = 5 m$
12. $£7.68 + 89p + \boxed{} = £25$
13. $7.25 km + 865 m + \boxed{} = 10 km$
14. $875 m\ell + 0.765 \ell + \boxed{} = 3 \ell$
15. $0.725 kg + 7685 g + \boxed{} = 5 kg$

C
Total these masses:

8 tonnes   275 kg   867.5 kg

Subtraction

Work out the answer in your head.

1 4.28 – 0.43
  a 3.75
  b 3.85
  c 3.95

2 6.27 – 0.99
  a 5.26
  b 5.27
  c 5.28

3 5.72 – 0.39
  a 5.31
  b 5.32
  c 5.33

A

Calculate the answers to these.

1 What is the difference between 1.5 and 0.725?

2 Subtract 0.677 from 2.0

3 Decrease 8.25 by 1.8

4 How much more than 21.7 is 27.07?

5 How much less than 6.128 is 4.8?

6 What must be added to 0.74 to make 1.631?

7 What must be subtracted from 13.6 to leave 6.994?

8 What is 4.776 subtracted from 20.1?

> When subtracting decimal numbers, line up the decimal points. Adding zeros sometimes helps.
>
> 6.45 – 3.136
>
>   6.450
> – 3.136

> You can always check a subtraction by addition:
>
> Check:
>
>   6.450   **3.314**
> – 3.136   + 3.136
>   **3.314**   6.450

B

What are the missing digits?

1
```
   2. □ 6 0
 –0. 9 7 □
 ─────────
   1. 3 8 4
```

2
```
   3 .7 1 □
 – □ .8 □ 6
 ─────────
   0. 8 4 4
```

3
```
   1 2 . □ 3
 – □ . 9 7 □
 ─────────
   6 . 8 5 8
```

Calculate the answers.

4 2.5 m – 1.79 m

5 3.0 kg – 1.626 kg

6 75 km – 24.65 km

7 6.2 g – 5.625 g

8 4.5 m – 128 cm

9 5.1 kg – 895 g

10 1.25 ℓ – 50 mℓ

C

Subtract 267 g from $2\frac{1}{4}$ kg.

Multiplication 1

Work out the answer in your head.

1. 0.7 × 0.8
   - a 5.6
   - b 0.56
   - c 0.056

2. 6.0 × 0.7
   - a 4.2
   - b 0.42
   - c 0.042

3. 0.4 × 9.0
   - a 3.6
   - b 0.36
   - c 0.036

A Calculate the answers to these.

1. 6348 × 8
2. 7064 × 7
3. 8519 × 6
4. 12765 × 4
5. 25067 × 5

6. 34.86 × 4
7. 48.07 × 6
8. 26.98 × 7
9. 125.66 × 5
10. 327.75 × 8

11. 4.625 × 6
12. 0.768 × 9
13. 7.552 × 6
14. 2.653 × 11
15. 0.4882 × 12

B Calculate these then check each answer.

1. 626 × 0.4
2. 375 × 0.7
3. 463 × 0.9
4. 2418 × 0.3
5. 4266 × 0.8

6. 3.44 × 0.2
7. 5.18 × 0.4
8. 4.395 × 0.7
9. 16.73 × 0.5
10. 39.35 × 0.6

11. 0.76 × 0.5
12. 0.44 × 0.7
13. 0.83 × 0.8
14. 0.237 × 0.6
15. 0.625 × 0.4

> When you multiply by a number that is less than 1, the answer will be less than you started with.
>
> 126 × 0.6 = 75.6
>
> Check: 0.6 is just over a half so the answer will be a little more than half of 126.

C Fabric cost £14.29 per metre.
What is the cost of 0.8 metres?

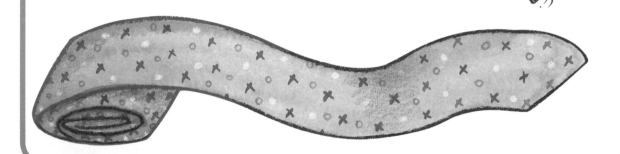

Multiplication 2

Warm up Work out each answer in your head.

1. 60 × 500
   - a 3000
   - b 30 000
   - c 300 000

2. 80 × 7000
   - a 56 000
   - b 560 000
   - c 5 600 000

3. 9000 × 300
   - a 27 000
   - b 270 000
   - c 2 700 000

A Calculate these and check each answer.

1. 165 × 65
2. 345 × 72
3. 707 × 55
4. 624 × 38
5. 928 × 86
6. 214 × 265
7. 865 × 764
8. 956 × 654
9. 712 × 256
10. 665 × 843

What are the missing numbers?

11. (46 × 65) + ☐ = 3000
12. (76 × 38) − ☐ = 2000
13. 76 × (85 − 28) = ☐
14. 63 × (68 + 74) = ☐
15. (85 − 32) × (38 + 88) = ☐

> When multiplying large numbers, either **estimate** first or **check** afterwards.
>
> 687 × 76
> Estimate: 700 × 80 = 56 000
> Answer: 687 × 76 = 52 212
>
> 328 × 279
> Answer: 328 × 279 = 91 512
> Check: 300 × 300 = 90 000

B Calculate the answers to these.

1. 225 × 5.6
2. 714 × 7.5
3. 208 × 6.9
4. 513 × 7.3
5. 865 × 2.8
6. 25.3 × 7.2
7. 81.8 × 9.3
8. 14.8 × 6.2
9. 30.6 × 5.6
10. 24.9 × 7.8
11. 2.76 × 2.6
12. 3.77 × 5.4
13. 8.55 × 7.3
14. 1.44 × 4.75
15. 6.25 × 6.25

> Multiplying by decimals is not too difficult if you are careful with the decimal point. Checking can help.
>
> 236 × 2.7 = 637.2
> Check: 240 × 3 = 720
>
> 15.27 × 6.8 = 103.836
> Check: 15 × 7 = 105

C Rope costs £3.49 per metre. What will 2.8 metres cost?

Division 1

Warm up

Work out the answer in your head.

1 5.6 ÷ 8	2 0.56 ÷ 8	3 0.056 ÷ 8
a 7.0	a 0.7	a 0.7
b 0.7	b 0.07	b 0.07
c 0.07	c 0.007	c 0.007

A

Work out the quotient to one decimal place.	Work out the quotient to two decimal places.	Work out the quotient to three decimal places.
1 346 ÷ 6	6 275 ÷ 8	11 903 ÷ 7
2 839 ÷ 9	7 3765 ÷ 6	12 6111 ÷ 5
3 1034 ÷ 7	8 573.9 ÷ 5	13 453.7 ÷ 8
4 4613 ÷ 8	9 447.1 ÷ 9	14 127.86 ÷ 9
5 7052 ÷ 3	10 603.5 ÷ 7	15 307.04 ÷ 6

> When dividing, you sometimes have to write the quotient to the nearest whole number or to one, two or three decimal places.
>
> $2654 ÷ 7 = 379.1428$
>
> to the nearest whole number = 379
> to one decimal place = 379.1
> to two decimal places = 379.14
> to three decimal places = 379.143

B

Calculate then check each answer.

Work out the quotient to one decimal place.	Work out the quotient to two decimal places.	Work out the quotient to three decimal places.
1 217 ÷ 0.4	6 78.5 ÷ 0.3	11 6.25 ÷ 0.7
2 407 ÷ 0.3	7 17.1 ÷ 0.8	12 4.01 ÷ 0.6
3 845 ÷ 0.8	8 70.4 ÷ 0.7	13 9.06 ÷ 0.9
4 601 ÷ 0.7	9 33.2 ÷ 0.5	14 12.63 ÷ 0.8
5 555 ÷ 0.9	10 57.7 ÷ 0.9	15 24.75 ÷ 0.5

> When you divide by less than 1, the answer will be more than you started with.
>
> $143 ÷ 0.6$ to two decimal places (multiply both numbers by 10)
> $1430 ÷ 6 = 238.33$

C

$7.4 ÷ \square = 9.25$

Which of these is the missing number?

0.2   0.4   0.6   0.8

Division 2

Work out the answer in your head.

1. 30 000 ÷ 500
   - a 60
   - b 600
   - c 6000

2. 5 600 000 ÷ 7000
   - a 80
   - b 800
   - c 8000

3. 27 000 ÷ 300
   - a 90
   - b 900
   - c 9000

A Write the quotients as decimals.

To one decimal place.	To two decimal places.	To three decimal places.
1 717 ÷ 19	6 3560 ÷ 77	11 1286 ÷ 125
2 884 ÷ 24	7 2175 ÷ 46	12 5389 ÷ 206
3 911 ÷ 35	8 8053 ÷ 66	13 4062 ÷ 303
4 629 ÷ 71	9 7002 ÷ 42	14 7219 ÷ 563
5 805 ÷ 56	10 5691 ÷ 93	15 9031 ÷ 646

When dividing large numbers, either **estimate** first or **check** afterwards.

687 ÷ 76
Estimate: 700 ÷ 80 ≈ 9
Answer: 9.039 (to three places of decimals)

5328 ÷ 279
Answer: 5328 ÷ 279 = 19.097 (to three places of decimals)
Check: 5000 × 300 ≈ 17

B Write quotients as decimals.
The answers to section A may help you.

To one decimal place.	To two decimal places.	To three decimal places.
1 717 ÷ 1.9	6 356.0 ÷ 7.7	11 12.86 ÷ 12.5
2 884 ÷ 2.4	7 217.5 ÷ 4.6	12 53.89 ÷ 20.6
3 911 ÷ 3.5	8 805.3 ÷ 6.6	13 40.62 ÷ 30.3
4 629 ÷ 7.1	9 700. ÷ 4.2	14 72.19 ÷ 56.3
5 805 ÷ 5.6	10 569.1 ÷ 9.3	15 90.1 ÷ 64.6

Dividing by decimals is not too difficult if you are careful with the decimal point. This check can help.

236 ÷ 2.7 (multiply both numbers by 10)
2360 ÷ 27 = 87.41
Check: 2400 × 30 ≈ 80

15.27 ÷ 6.8 (multiply both numbers by 10)
152.7 ÷ 68 = 2.25
Check: 150 × 70 ≈ 2

C What is the missing number?

$$(1000 ÷ \boxed{}) + 0.5 = 0.75$$

What is the length of side of each square?

1 Area = 36 cm²   a 18 cm   b 9 cm   c 6 cm

2 Area = 100 cm²   a 50 cm   b 25 cm   c 10 cm

3 Area = 144 cm²   a 72 cm   b 36 cm   c 12 cm

A Calculate the areas of these shapes.

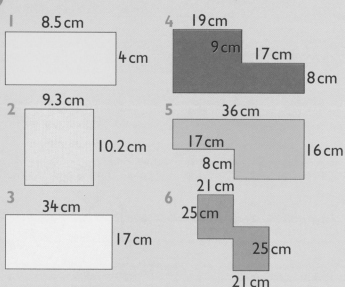

1 8.5 cm   4 cm

2 9.3 cm   10.2 cm

3 34 cm   17 cm

4 19 cm, 9 cm, 17 cm, 8 cm

5 36 cm, 17 cm, 8 cm, 16 cm

6 21 cm, 25 cm, 25 cm, 21 cm

Sometimes you need to split a shape up into rectangles to find its area.

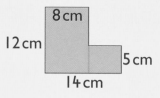

8 cm
12 cm
5 cm
14 cm

Area of the large rectangle:
12 × 8 = 96 cm²
Area of the small rectangle:
5 × 6 = 30 cm²
Total area = 126 cm²

B Calculate the shaded areas.

1 36 cm, 18 cm, 12 cm, 25 cm

2 12 cm, 5.5 cm, 5.5 cm, 12 cm

3 32 cm, 25 cm, 6 cm, 25 cm

4 4.5 cm, 9 cm, 20 cm, 16.5 cm

Sometimes you need to subtract to find an area.

16 cm
6 cm
5 cm 14 cm

Area of the large rectangle:
16 × 14 = 224 cm²
Area of the small rectangle:
5 × 6 = 30 cm²
Total shaded area = 194 cm²

C A rectangular lawn measures 8.5 m by 6 m.
It has a 4 m square flowerbed cut out of the middle.
What is the area of grass?

Area 2

What is the area of the red part?

1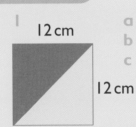
12 cm
12 cm

  a 144 cm²
  b 36 cm²
  c 72 cm²

2
18 cm
10 cm

  a 45 cm²
  b 90 cm²
  c 180 cm²

3 15 cm
10 cm

  a 75 cm²
  b 150 cm²
  c 35½ cm²

A Calculate the areas of these shapes.

Here is a formula to find the area of right-angled triangles.

H
B

$$\text{Area} = \tfrac{1}{2}(H \times B)$$

1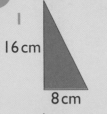
16 cm
8 cm

4
9 cm   9 cm

2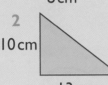
10 cm
13 cm

5
14 cm   21 cm

3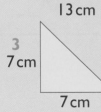
7 cm
7 cm

6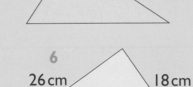
26 cm   18 cm

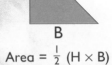

B

1 Find the length, breadth and height of box A.

2 What is the total surface area of the box A?   BOX A

3 Find the length, breadth and height of box B.

4 What is the total surface area of the box B?   BOX B

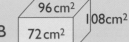
144 cm²
120 cm²
120 cm²

96 cm²
108 cm²
72 cm²

C What is the area of this shape?

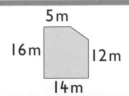
5 m
16 m
12 m
14 m

Volume

Warm up Try to answer these in your head.

1 **40 × 70 × 50**
 a 1400
 b 14 000
 c 140 000

2 **80 × 60 × 20**
 a 9600
 b 96 000
 c 960 000

3 **80 × 50 × 40**
 a 1600
 b 16 000
 c 160 000

A Calculate the volumes of these boxes.

1
6 cm 6 cm 6 cm

2
6 cm 8 cm 5 cm

3
15 cm 18 cm 12 cm

4
26 cm 36 cm 13 cm

5
50 cm 70 cm 40 cm

6
108 cm 120 cm 85 cm

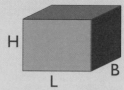

Here is a formula to find the volume of a cube or cuboid.

H L B

Volume = area of base × height
Volume = L × B × H
Remember volume uses cm³ or m³.

B The table shows the sizes of some cuboids. Some of the dimensions are missing. Copy and complete the table.

	Length L	Breadth B	Height H	Volume V
1	9 cm	6 cm	7 cm	
2		7 cm	10 cm	840 cm³
3	20 cm		12 cm	3840 cm³
4	25 cm	20 cm		12 500 cm³
5	30 cm	27 cm	24 cm	

C Work out how many 2 cm cubes will fit into the box.

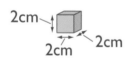

2 cm 2 cm 2 cm

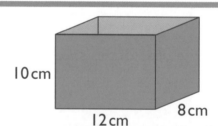

10 cm 12 cm 8 cm

Circumference

1 **3.14 × 10**
   a 0.314
   b 3.140
   c 31.4

2 **3.14 × 6**
   a 16.84
   b 18.84
   c 20.84

3 **3.14 × 24**
   a 75.36
   b 78.36
   c 80.36

A Measure the diameter of each circle to the nearest centimetre.
Calculate the circumference of each circle.

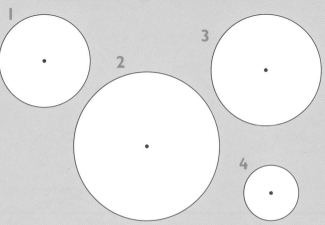

Here is a formula to find the circumference of a circle:
Circumference = π × Diameter
C = πD

π is called pi. It is a letter in the Greek alphabet.
π is the number of times the diameter will divide into the circumference.
For all circles:
Circumference ÷ Diameter = 3.14
π = 3.14 (to two decimal places)

B The radius is shown. Calculate the circumference of each circle.

1 R = 15 cm   4 R = 5 cm

2 R = 12 cm   5 R = 8 cm

3 R = 20 cm   6 R = 2.5 cm

Find the approximate circumference first.
Radius = 2 cm so diameter = 4 cm

π ≈ 3

Approximate circumference 3 × 4 = 12 cm
Actual circumference 3.14 × 4 = 12.56 cm

C A wheel has a diameter of 1 metre.
How far will it roll in 10 turns?
Use π = 3.14

1 m

Area 3

Warm up Calculate the squares.

1. 12^2
   - a 121
   - b 144
   - c 164

2. 15^2
   - a 125
   - b 165
   - c 225

3. 25^2
   - a 425
   - b 525
   - c 625

A Measure the radius of each circle to the nearest centimetre.
Calculate the area of each circle.

1

2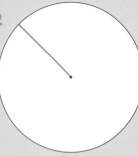

> Here is a formula to find the area of a circle:
> **Area = π × Radius²**
> **A = πR²**
> π is called pi. It is a letter in the Greek alphabet.
> π is the number of times the diameter of a circle will divide into its circumference.
> π = 3.14 (to two decimal places)

B The diameter of each circle is shown.
Calculate each area.

1 D = 12 cm   4 D = 6 m

2 D = 20 cm   5 D = 10 m

3 D = 30 cm   6 D = 2.4 m

> Find the approximate area first.
> Diameter = 8 cm so radius = 4 cm
>
> π ≈ 3
>
> Approximate area:
> $3 \times 4^2 = 48\,cm^2$
> Actual area:
> $3.14 \times 16 = 50.24\,cm^2$

C Here is a plan of a garden.
What is the area of the circular flowerbed?
Use π = 3.14

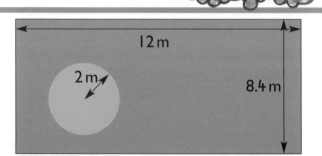

12 m

2 m

8.4 m

Comparing units

1 **feet**
   a ounces
   b inches
   c pints

2 **gallons**
   a pints
   b yards
   c tons

3 **pounds**
   a feet
   b inches
   c ounces

A

8 km ≈ 5 miles
30 cm ≈ 1 foot
$2\frac{1}{2}$ cm ≈ 1 inch
30 g ≈ 1 ounce
1 kg ≈ $2\frac{1}{4}$ pounds
$4\frac{1}{2}$ litres ≈ 1 gallon
1 litre ≈ $1\frac{3}{4}$ pints
1 gallon = 8 pints
1 foot = 12 inches
1 pound = 16 ounces

Change these to approximate imperial units.

1  PARIS 49km

2 1.5 L

3  60 cm

Change these to approximate metric units.

4 CARDIFF 63 Miles

5  pint

6 5 lb

You will see both imperial and metric units in use. These rhymes will help you compare metric and imperial units:
- A metre is just three foot three, it's longer than a yard, you see.
- Two and a quarter pounds of jam, is round about one kilogram.
- A litre of water's about a pint and three quarters.

B

Write your answers to the nearest whole unit.

Convert to metric units.

1 56 pounds
2 12 ounces
3 4 gallons
4 250 miles

Convert to imperial units.

5 30 litres
6 15 kilograms
7 750 grams
8 312 kilometres

Sometimes you need to be more accurate when changing between metric and imperial units.

1 km = 0.62 miles	1 mile = 1.61 km
1 kg = 2.20 pounds	1 pound = 0.45 kg
1 g = 0.04 ounces	1 ounce = 28.45 g
1 ℓ = 0.22 gallons	1 gallon = 4.55 ℓ

C

Which is the heavier?

 ½ kilo

 1 lb

Measurement problems

Which is the equivalent measurement?

1 **0.005 m**
  a 5 dm
  b 5 cm
  c 5 mm

2 **0.005 km**
  a 5 m
  b 5 cm
  c 5 dm

3 **0.005 tonnes**
  a 5 kg
  b 5 g
  c 50 g

A

Draw the shape that has:

1 A perimeter three-quarters of this perimeter. Write the dimensions on your rectangle.

2 A radius one-half of this circle. Write the dimensions on your circle.

When constructing the new shape, use a sharp pencil, ruler, set square and compasses to help.

B

Calculate the area of each shape.

1

2

$\pi = 3.14$

- Sometimes you have to measure before calculating.
- Take whatever measurements you need.
- Choose whether to work in cm or mm.
- Be as accurate as you can.

C

Measure then calculate the area of this right-angled triangle in cm².

Percentage problems 1

1   $\dfrac{2}{5}$
   a   20%
   b   30%
   c   40%

2   $\dfrac{18}{20}$
   a   90%
   b   80%
   c   70%

3   $\dfrac{14}{25}$
   a   28%
   b   42%
   c   56%

A   Calculate the answers.

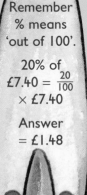

1   For each 120 kg of food made there is 5% wastage. How many kilograms of wastage is there for each 120 kg?

2   In each 120 litres of fruit squash there is 96 litres of water. What percentage is this?

3   For each 75 tonnes of stone taken from a quarry, 63 tonnes are sold for making roads. What percentage is this?

4   A company makes 5000 parts each day. 24% of the parts are exported. How many parts is this?

5   A factory spends £6200 on fuel. Gas is 14%, oil is 48% and the rest is electricity. How much is spent on each type of fuel?

Remember
% means
'out of 100'.

20% of
£7.40 $= \dfrac{20}{100}$
$\times$ £7.40

Answer
= £1.48

B   What is the total value of the coins in the bottle?

1   £2   2   50p   3   20p   4   10p   5   2p

6   What percentage of 1p coins is in the bottle?

7   How many 1p coins are in the bottle?

8   How much money is in the bottle?

There are 500 coins in this large bottle.

3% are £2 coins
5% are £1 coins
10% are 50p coins
6% are 20p coins
12% are 10p coins
15% are 5p coins
35% are 2p coins
the rest are 1p coins

C   Look at the newspaper headline.

How much did the dogs' home receive?

$2\tfrac{1}{2}$ % of £1200 windfall given to dogs' home.

Percentage problems 2

What is 20% of each amount?

1 £9
  a £2.00
  b £1.80
  c £1.60

2  £15
  a £5
  b £3.50
  c £3

3 £7.50
  a £1.50
  b £2.00
  c £2.50

A Calculate the sale price of each item.

> You can reduce amounts by a percentage.
> Reduce £16 by 20%:
> 20% of £16 = £3.20
> New price £16 − £3.20 = £12.80

1  £9.50
20% reduction

2  £22
15% reduction

3  £17
30% reduction

4  £124
45% reduction

5 £36
$33\frac{1}{3}$% reduction

6 £8
$7\frac{1}{2}$% reduction

B Calculate each sale price to the nearest penny.

> Sometimes you work to the nearest penny.
> Reduce £33.25 by 15%:
> 15% of £33.25 = £4.99 (to nearest penny)
> New price £33.25 − £4.99 = £28.26

1 £245.99
20% off

2 £189.50
5% off

3 £366.99
10% off

4 £30.78
$7\frac{1}{2}$% off

5 £1109
$12\frac{1}{2}$% off

6  £824.99
$17\frac{1}{2}$% off

C What is the total cost of buying one of each item?

Spend between £5 and £10 = **10% off**
Spend over £10 = **$12\frac{1}{2}$% off**
Cups **£2.99** each   Bowls **£3.50** each
Saucers **£1.20** each   Plates **£2.70** each

Percentage problems 3

Warm up

What is $2\frac{1}{2}$% of each amount?

1 **£10**
   a £0.75
   b £0.50
   c £0.25

2 **£30**
   a £0.75
   b £0.50
   c £0.25

3 **£100**
   a £1.50
   b £2.00
   c £2.50

A

Answer these to the nearest penny.

Winsack Building Society pay $4\frac{1}{2}$% interest per year. What will the total amount be at the end of the year for each of these:

	Jan 1	Dec 31		Jan 1	Dec 31
1	£80	?	5	£38.50	?
2	£160	?	6	£205.76	?
3	£2056	?	7	£7398.99	?
4	£12750	?	8	£50250.25	?

> You can increase amounts by a percentage.
>
> Increase £16 by 20%:
>
> 20% of £16 = £3.20
>
> New price
> £16 + £3.20 = £19.20

B

Work out the missing numbers. **Estimate   Check**

1 12% of ☐ = £15.00   _____ _____

2 45% of ☐ = £369.00   _____ _____

3 82% of ☐ = £779.00   _____ _____

4 ☐ % of £645 = £39.75   _____ _____

5 ☐ % of £764 = £320.88   _____ _____

6 ☐ % of £968 = £822.80   _____ _____

> • In these problems, estimate each missing number.
> • Use a calculator to check the estimate.
> • Estimate again and check.
> • See how many estimates you need before finding the exact answer.

C

Which is the better offer:

$33\frac{1}{3}$% off or a reduction of $\frac{3}{10}$?

£24.84

Ratio and proportion

Work out the following.

1. $\frac{4}{5}$ of 120
   - a 24
   - b 72
   - c 96

2. $\frac{3}{4}$ of 700
   - a 175
   - b 350
   - c 525

3. $\frac{5}{8}$ of 4000
   - a 500
   - b 1500
   - c 2500

A Write the ratio of ■ to ▲ .

1.

2.

3.

In a safari park there are 16 llamas, 10 lions, 8 monkeys, 6 tigers and 4 giraffes.

What is ratio of:

4. lions to tigers

5. lions to giraffes

6. monkeys to lions

> A ratio is how we compare two quantities.
> Ratios are written like this 3:4. It means for every 3 of one thing there will be 4 of something else.
>
> You can cancel ratios like fractions:
> 6:8 is the same ratio as 3:4

B A map has a scale of 1:50 000.

1. What would a map distance of 3 cm be on the ground?

2. How many centimetres would represent 10 km?

3. Which is larger scale map: 1:25 000 or 1:50 000?

Paste has be diluted in the ratio 2:3 (paste:water).

4. How much water is needed to dilute 100 mℓ of paste?

5. How much paste is needed to make up a 1 litre mix?

> Ratios and scales are often used in measuring
> 1 cm: 10 metres is the same scale as:
>
> 1 cm: 1000 cm
>
> and this is written as a fraction as $\frac{1}{1000}$

C Here is part of a recipe for four people.
Write the recipe for six people.

6 oz lentils (175 g)
4 oz split peas (110 g)
1 pint water (570 ml)
2 tablespoons melted butter
1 medium onion
$\frac{3}{4}$ teaspoon mixed herbs

Probability

Warm up When rolling a dice what are the chances of:

1. rolling a 6?
   - a even
   - b 1 in 6
   - c 1 in 3

2. rolling an odd number?
   - a evens
   - b 1 in 6
   - c 1 in 3

3. rolling a number greater than 3?
   - a evens
   - b 1 in 6
   - c 1 in 3

A Draw probability lines like this: 0 |——————|—————| 1

0 has no chance of the event happening.
1 is certain to happen.

Draw arrows on probability lines to show the chance of the spinner stopping in section A.

> A probability line shows the chance of something happening.
>
> impossible   certain
> 0 |——————|——————| 1
>   ↑
> The arrows shows that the chance is 50/50, or evens.

1

2

3

B Two spinners have numbers on them as shown in the picture. Which total is most likely to be scored?

It will help to complete a table showing all the possible totals.

> Sometimes you have to work out which thing will be most likely to happen. It doesn't necessarily mean that it will always happen most often.

spinner 1

+	1	2	3	4	5	6
1						
2						
3						
4						
5						
6						

spinner 2

C There are 36 beads in a box. 6 beads are red, 12 beads are blue, 10 beads are green and the rest are yellow.

What are the chances of taking out a bead that is not red?

41

Angles

Warm up

Which type of angle are these?

1.
   - a acute
   - b obtuse
   - c reflex

2.
   - a acute
   - b obtuse
   - c reflex

3.
   - a acute
   - b obtuse
   - c reflex

A

Calculate the size of the missing angles.

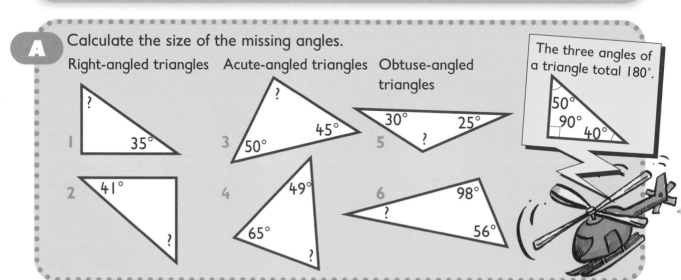

Right-angled triangles   Acute-angled triangles   Obtuse-angled triangles

The three angles of a triangle total 180°.

50° 90° 40°

1. ? 35°

2. 41° ?

3. ? 50° 45°

4. 49° 65° ?

5. 30° 25° ?

6. 98° ? 56°

B

Calculate the size of the mystery angle.

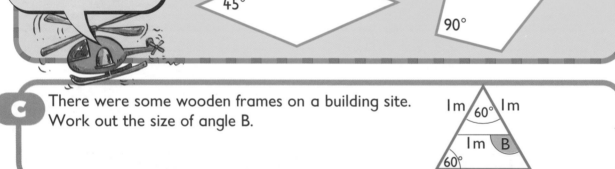

The four angles of a quadrilateral total 360°

75° 90° 95° 100°

1. trapezium
   ? 60° 60°

2. rhombus
   ? 45°

3. parallelogram
   ? 135°

4. kite
   115° 90° ?

C

There were some wooden frames on a building site. Work out the size of angle B.

1m 60° 1m 1m B 60°

42

Bearings

How many degrees are between these directions, turning clockwise?

1 N and W
   a 90°
   b 180°
   c 270°

2 E and N
   a 90°
   b 180°
   c 270°

3 W and E
   a 90°
   b 180°
   c 270°

A Which bearing is the same as:

1 SW   3 S   5 W

2 NW   4 SE   6 E

> Remember bearings are always measured from North in a clockwise direction.
>
> There are always three digits in a bearing.
>
> A bearing of 045° is the same as NE.

B What is the bearing of each buoy from the boat?

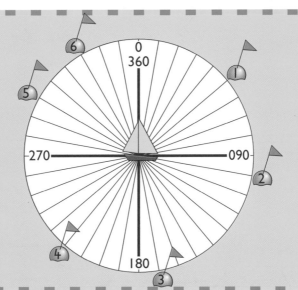

C Which of these is the approximate bearing of Stirling from Edinburgh?

205°   265°   295°   345°

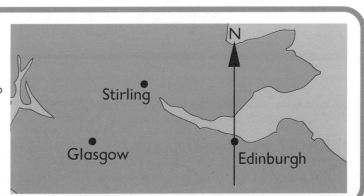

Polygons

Warm up What is the name of each quadrilateral?

1 a rhombus
   b kite
   c parallelogram

2 a rhombus
   b trapezium
   c parallelogram

3 a kite
   b rhombus
   c parallelogram

A Write how many different ways each shape fits into its outline.

To fit shapes into outlines, think about rotation around the centre and flipping shapes over.

B Find the congruent triangles.

1

Congruent shapes are identical in shape and size. Their colours or positions might be different.

2

C Look at the shapes.
Write which of these statements are true.

A They are all quadrilaterals.

C They all have the same area.

B They all have line symmetry.

D They all contain at least one right angle.

Positions

Warm up What is the red line in relation to the blue line?

1
a parallel
b perpendicular
c oblique

2
a parallel
b perpendicular
c oblique

3
a parallel
b perpendicular
c oblique

A

1 Draw the triangle ABC that has these coordinates:

  A (2,8)   B (1,1)   C (5,3)

2 Draw its reflection when a mirror is placed down the y-axis.

3 Label the new triangle A′ B′ C′

4 Write the coordinates of A′, B′ and C′.

- Horizontal coordinates are along the x-axis.
- Vertical coordinates are along the y-axis.
- In the second quadrant the x coordinate will be negative for example (−3,2).

y-axis

second quadrant | first quadrant

x-axis

B

1 Draw the triangle ABC that has these coordinates:

  A (−2,4)   B (−1,1)   C (−4,0)

2 Rotate the triangle for 180° about the coordinate (0,0). Use tracing paper if that helps.

3 Draw the position of the new triangle.

4 Label the triangle A′ B′ C′.

5 Write the coordinates of A′, B′ and C′.

- Coordinates can be plotted in four quadrants.
- In the third quadrant, both coordinates will be negative for example (−3, −4).

y-axis

second quadrant | first quadrant

x-axis

third quadrant | fourth quadrant

C

Here are three coordinates of a parallelogram ABCD.

  A (−4,3)   B (4,1)   C (4, −4)

What are the coordinates of corner D?

Data 1

A

The pie chart shows what 200 children liked in their sandwiches.

This pie chart shows what 200 children liked to read.

1 What percentage of children liked cheese filling?

2 What percentage of children liked crisp filling?

3 How many children liked jam?

4 What percentage of children liked sport's books?

5 What percentage of children liked adventure stories?

6 How many children read humorous books?

B

The graph shows children's heights.

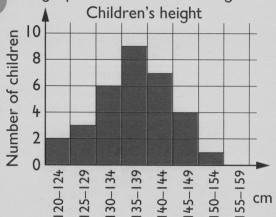

This graph shows children's heights and shoe sizes.
Each cross represents a child.

1 How many children are between 125 cm and 140 cm tall?

2 How many children are taller than 130 cm?

3 Which height is the mode?

4 How many children took size 5 and were under 140 cm tall?

5 How many children were taller than 144 cm?

6 How many children took more than size 6?

Data 2

A Look at the bar graph.

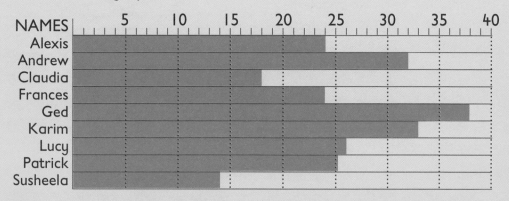

| NAMES | | 5 | 10 | 15 | 20 | 25 | 30 | 35 | 40 |

1 What was the range of marks?   3 What was the mean score?

2 What was the median score?

B This scale converts between Centigrade and Fahrenheit temperatures.

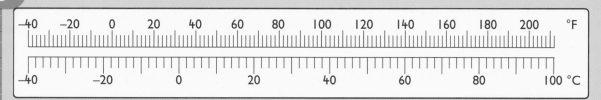

1 32°F = ?°C   2 10°C = ?°F   3 −15°F = ?°C

C The graph shows what happened when a ball was thrown between two people.

1 How long was it travelling upwards?

2 How high was it after 3.5 seconds?

3 From its highest point, how long did it take to drop to 10 metres?

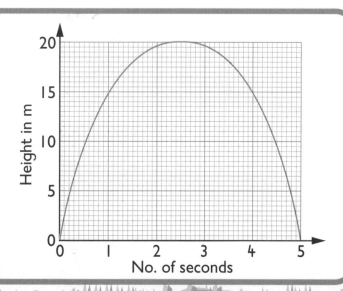

Brainbox

Write the answers to these problems.
Try to answer each one in your head.
Some questions are quite hard.

1 What is area of this right-angled triangle?

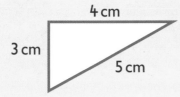

2 How many mm in 2.5 dm?

3 What is 15^2?

4 What is 45% of £5?

5 How many minutes are there from 22:42 to 00:36?

6 What is the decimal quotient of 17 ÷ 8?

7 What is half of 3.5?

8 What is $\frac{3}{8}$ of 120?

9 What fraction of 5 m is 25 cm?

10 What is 0.12 × 0.06?

11 If the perimeter of a square is 1 m, what is its area?

12 How many mℓ are there in 12.5 cℓ?

13 What is 350 × 14?

14 What is the difference between 1.02 and 0.7?

15 What is double $\frac{7}{8}$?

16 What is double 600 plus 41 minus 39?

17 What is 3.97 + 4.58?

18 What must be added to 7.36 to total 7.4?

19 What must be subtracted from 0.5 to leave 0.19?

20 What is 39 000 ÷ 40?

How did you do?
Well done if you scored more than 10.
More than 15 is fantastic!